Everyday Beauty

by Kirsten Anderson
illustrated by Matthew Archambault

Table of Contents

Chapter 1
What Is a Perfect Picture?

The hummingbird flew near the wildflowers. Carly kept still and quiet. She stared into her camera as she waited. She flicked a fly away with her finger. The hummingbird flew near a flower, but the flower was not red enough. Another flower was too small. Finally, the hummingbird stopped over the largest, reddest flower. Carly began to take pictures. She was certain that these pictures would be good.

Carly ran home and <u>uploaded</u> the pictures onto her computer. When she saw the pictures on the computer screen, she was disappointed. Carly opened her photo journal.

She wrote, "My hummingbird pictures are not good. The wings of the bird are unclear. I can't see much <u>detail</u> on the flower. The bird is not close to the flower in any shot. Why don't the pictures look like I thought they would?"

"Carly, it is time for dinner," said her brother Brad.

<u>uploaded</u>: to transfer or move from a camera to a computer
<u>detail</u>: fine or tiny parts of something

Brad stood in the doorway, tapping his fingers on the door.

"Look at these pictures." Carly pointed to the computer screen.

"They are nice," Brad said.

"That is the problem," Carly said. She sighed. "They should be more exciting. It is a beautiful day. The bird is exciting and the flowers are gorgeous. Here." She gave Brad her camera. "You can have it. I am done with photography."

Brad waited a minute. Then he gave Carly her camera back.

"You quit photography almost every day," Brad said. "Stop worrying."

"I just want to take beautiful pictures of beautiful things in wonderful places," Carly said.

"Maybe you should take ugly pictures of ugly things in dull places," Brad said and smiled.

"That is not funny," Carly said.

"I'm about to feed your barbecue to Rusty and Scout," Mom called. "Come to dinner."

Brad rushed out the door.

Carly looked at the hummingbird pictures again. She had always been interested in cameras and photographs. Her father had let her take pictures with his camera as soon as she could hold one. At first it was just fun. She took pictures of anything. But now Carly wanted something more.

"I want to take the kinds of pictures that make people stop and look," she thought.

"Rusty is eating your dinner!" Brad yelled.

Chapter 2
A Visitor

"Carly, I am going to the <u>stockroom</u>," Dad said. "Call me if you need help."

"Sure," said Carly.

Carly and her family lived near Fort Peck Lake in Montana. Her parents owned a fishing and camping supply store. During the summer, swarms of tourists came to fish at the lake and camp in the Charles M. Russell National Wildlife Refuge.

<u>stockroom</u>: a place to keep supplies or things to sell

Carly loved talking to visitors about the area. Fort Peck Lake was so big that she could not see where it ended. Ducks flew across the surface of the lake. People could often see geese strutting along the shore. Kingfishers sat on the rocks at the edge of the water. Carly saw deer, raccoons, owls, and foxes. She spent hours looking for things to shoot with her camera. Each season everything changed. She was never bored.

Sometimes Carly thought about other places she had gone. She had visited her cousins in Seattle many times. The streets in Seattle were filled with cars, and the houses were close together. Carly wondered what it must be like in Chicago or New York. People were packed into apartment buildings. She looked at pictures of skyscrapers. She thought the big, gray buildings were dull. Carly thought it must be hard to be a photographer in the city.

---

packed into: to have many people or things in a space

Just then a young couple came into the store. The man got some batteries for his camera. The woman told Carly that they <u>were</u> going to Fort Peck Dam. The dam had been built in the 1930s. It held back the Missouri River, and made Fort Peck Lake.

Carly frowned. "Really? The dam is a little boring."

"Oh, that is not true!" the woman said. "Look."

She pulled a book out of her backpack. She opened it and handed it to Carly.

Carly looked at the photograph. She had never seen the dam look like this. It looked like a giant castle. Its towers seemed to touch the clouds in the sky. At the bottom of the picture were two tiny people. They made the dam look even bigger and more grand.

"Who took this picture?" Carly asked.

"Margaret Bourke-White," said the woman. "It was taken in 1936."

Carly wrote the name of the photographer on a piece of paper. She was excited to learn more about the picture.

Clue: The linking verb <u>were</u> is plural. It agrees with its subject, the noun *they*. Can you find other examples of subject-verb agreement on this page?

Chapter 3
Carly Learns from the Past

When Carly got home, she looked on the Internet for the Fort Peck Dam picture. She printed it and looked at it more closely.

Carly wrote in her photo journal. "The dam is not beautiful. But I think it has something to do with the <u>angle</u> or position of the picture. Maybe it is the clouds. Did the photographer wait for the perfect day to take the picture?"

Clue: <u>Angle</u> may be a new word. Look at the context, or the sentence, in which it is used. Can you guess what the meaning of <u>angle</u> is?

Carly searched the Internet for other Margaret Bourke-White photographs. The pictures were of ordinary bridges, towers, and buildings. These were not things Carly usually thought were interesting. But these pictures caught her attention.

"Maybe I like them because they are black and white," Carly wrote. She changed her own pictures from color to black and white on the computer. That was not the answer to her problem. Her pictures just looked pale and faded.

The pictures that interested Carly the most showed things that were not really amazing. Margaret had taken pictures of a Cleveland steel factory in the late 1920s. It was not a very exciting subject. It was just the factory at work. Still, Carly loved the pictures. She especially loved the one of a giant ladle pouring liquid steel. The light, shadows, and size of everything made it all seem glorious.

Carly printed the Margaret Bourke-White photographs she found. She pasted them on the wall to make a collage. She stared at them, and tried to find the secret to photography.

She wrote in her photo journal: "Maybe great pictures are not about looking for beautiful things. Maybe great pictures are also about looking for beauty in everyday things. Maybe anything can be beautiful."

Carly looked at the collage again and smiled. She was ready to start over.

Chapter 4
Carly Tries Something New

The next morning Carly took her camera and ran out to the porch. The family had cleaned out the basement and attic. A pile of stuff was on the porch. There were games, books, lamps, and sports equipment. The dogs slept in the middle of it.

Carly knelt down on the porch. She took pictures of everything. She tried different angles. She looked for shadows and patches of sun.

Carly kept her camera out as she walked to the store. She took pictures of cars, gates, and the empty sidewalks and streets. She took pictures of puddles and rocks. She took some pictures from close up and some from far away. When she got to the store, she picked up a group of fishing poles. She leaned them against a wall on the porch. Then she took pictures of them. She went into the store and took pictures of the counter. She knelt down on the floor and took pictures of the wooden floorboards.

"What are you doing?" Dad asked.

"I am trying something new," Carly said.

When Carly went home, she uploaded her pictures onto the computer. Some were not very good. Others were different. The fishing poles looked gigantic. The floorboards had contrasting patches of sun and shadows. This made them look like part of a train track.

Carly asked Brad to look at the pictures.

"Are those fishing poles?" he asked. He stared closely at one picture.

---

contrasting: very different

"Yes," Carly said.

"They look like they are big enough to hold up a building. That is a good picture," he said.

"Ugly things in dull places." Carly reminded him by repeating what he said to her before.

She printed out her pictures. Then she hung them next to the collage of Margaret Bourke-White photos.

Carly wrote in her photo journal: "It does not matter what you shoot with your camera. It is how you see it. You can see something lots of different ways. That can be better than seeing something one beautiful way."

Comprehension Check

Summarize

Complete a Character Web with the class. Summarize the story. You can use the chart to help you organize your ideas.

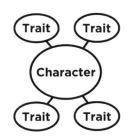

Think and Compare

1. Carly makes a collage of photographs. She tries to find the secret of the photographs. How do her thoughts change as she looks at the collage? *(Analyze Character)*

2. Carly takes photographs of Fort Peck Lake. If you were taking pictures of Fort Peck Lake, what would you photograph? Why? *(Apply)*

3. Look at the photographs by Margaret Bourke-White in Chapter 3. How do you think photographs can make ordinary things look glorious? *(Evaluate)*